ROS

LifeStories 3

.WITHDRAWN

New Readers Press

LifeStories 3
ISBN 978-1-56420-404-2
Copyright © 2003 New Readers Press
New Readers Press
Division of ProLiteracy Worldwide
1320 Jamesville Avenue, Syracuse, New York 13210
www.newreaderspress.com

Printed in the United States of America
9 8 7 6 5 4 3 2

All proceeds from the sale of New Readers Press materials
support literacy programs in the United States and worldwide.

Acquisitions Editor: Paula Schlusberg
Content Editor: Terrie Lipke
Copy Editor: Marcia Hough
Production Director: Heather Witt
Designer: Kimbrly Koennecke
Illustrations: Linda Tiff
Production Specialist: Jeffrey R. Smith
Cover Design: Andrea Woodbury

Contents

A Lesson in Learning

Stan was having coffee with Diep and Yolette after their computer class. Yolette asked, "Have you noticed that Roberto never takes notes?"

"I take so many notes my fingers get sore," said Stan. "How can he remember everything in the lesson without writing it down?"

"Here he comes," said Diep. "Let's ask."

Stan waved and said, "Come join us, Roberto." Stan pulled out an empty chair, and Roberto sat down. "Tell us something. How can you remember everything from the lectures without taking notes?"

Roberto smiled. "I just listen," he said. "After class I think about what I heard. And, if I can, I talk about it with someone."

"Wow," said Stan. "I can't remember anything unless I see it in writing. I'd rather read a book than listen to a lecture. But it does help me remember the lesson if I talk about it, too."

Yolette thought for a minute. "When I learn something new, I have to practice it right away. If I only try to memorize it, it just flies out of my head."

Stan turned to Roberto. "I can learn better if I talk things over with people. It's good to share ideas or ask each other questions. Why don't we start a study group?"

Roberto smiled. "I would like that very much, if I could find the time. I work in the evenings, and I like to spend weekends with my family."

Diep said, "I tried a study group once, and it just confused me. I learn better if I study alone." She shook her head. "Isn't it interesting how we each have a different style of learning?"

"Everyone is unique," Yolette said. She smiled. "Wouldn't life be dull if we were all the same? As for me, I have to listen, and read, and take notes. Then I like to discuss the lesson, too. But I do my best thinking while I'm on a long walk." Yolette stood up. "See you later," she said. "I think I'm going to walk home." She threw her empty cup in the trash can and headed out the door.

Save It or Lose It

The shoe store closed early on Saturday evenings. Yolette decided to stay late one Saturday and work on the computer. She looked at the pile of returned sale fliers. She addressed most of those herself, by hand. Now she was going to use this quiet time to make a database for a new customer mailing list. Lou would be so surprised when he came in Monday morning.

Yolette turned on the computer. She learned in class how to create a simple database. She decided to sort the customers by six categories: name, address, brand of shoes bought, sex, age, and sport.

Yolette entered the information, one customer at a time. She worked for more than three hours. Then the phone rang. She picked up the phone, but it was a wrong number.

When Yolette went back to the computer, the screen was blank! She hit *Enter*, but nothing happened. It seemed like the computer had shut itself off. Yolette didn't know what to do. She pushed the button to restart the computer.

The computer hummed and came back to life. Yolette looked for her new database file. It wasn't there. "Oh, no," she moaned. "This can't be happening."

Yolette called Diep to see if she knew how to find the file. She told Diep what happened.

"Did you save your work as you went along?" Diep asked.

"Oh no, I forgot," Yolette answered.

"How much work did you do before the phone rang?" asked Diep.

"I typed for three hours," cried Yolette.

"Don't you remember the first rule we learned in class?" Diep asked.

"What rule?" asked Yolette.

"*Save often*," Diep told her. "You never know when the power will go out or the computer will crash. And if your work is not saved, it just disappears."

"I can't believe I forgot to save," said Yolette. "Now what do I do?"

"Take a deep breath," said Diep. "And then start over."

Rules to Live By

Yolette was just getting home from work the next day. As she walked in the door the phone started ringing. When she answered, it was Diep. She sounded like she was going to cry.

"Something horrible happened," Diep said. "I don't know what to do."

"Has something happened to one of your children?" Yolette asked.

"No," Diep said. "But something might happen to all of us. We may lose our apartment. We are about to be evicted!"

"Why?" Yolette asked. "Haven't you been paying your rent?"

"I always pay my rent on time," Diep said. "But the apartment manager says I haven't paid for two months."

"Do you have receipts for the payments?" Yolette asked.

"He gave me receipts, but I didn't keep them," Diep said.

"Oh, no," Yolette said. "Diep, you taught me a lesson about the importance of saving. Now I have a lesson for you!"

Diep sighed, "I think I know what it is."

"Uh huh," said Yolette, nodding. "*Save your receipts for at least a year.* Then if there is any question about what you've paid, you have proof. I keep all my receipts in a file folder that has pockets for every month."

"That is good advice," said Diep. "But it is too late. Saving won't help me now."

"Maybe not," said Yolette. "But remember when we talked about different learning styles? I think when you learn a lesson by experience you never forget it. It worked for me. I save everything on my computer now! And you will start saving your receipts."

Busy Signals

Stan Wolanski had some questions about his Social Security card. He also wanted to check his savings account balance. He wanted to call his friend Nancy and ask her to go to a movie. And then he planned to call the theater and see what movies were playing.

Stan called Nancy's work number first. He was looking forward to talking with her. He thought someone answered the phone, but what he heard was, "All our lines are busy right now. Your call is important to us. Your call will be answered in the order in which it was received." Stan hung up.

He decided to make his other calls and then call Nancy back. He dialed the number for Social Security. He heard a click and then, "Thank you for calling Social Security. If you wish to conduct your business in English, press 1. For Spanish, press 2. To hear a list of our services, press 3. . . ." Stan hung up. "I'll just go to the local office," he muttered to himself.

Next Stan called the bank. After a few rings a voice said, "Welcome to County Bank's 24-hour telephone teller. If you are calling from a touch-tone phone, press 1 now. For checking account information, press 2. For loan applications, press 3. . . ." Stan gritted his teeth and hung up.

Next Stan dialed the number for the theater. A voice said, "Tonight on screen one, 'Silent Wish' is playing at 2:20, 4:40, 7:00, and 9:20. On screen two. . . ." Stan slammed the phone down. He had made four calls, yet he had not spoken to one person.

With a sigh he called Nancy's work number again. This time the voice said, "Our office is now closed. Office hours are from. . . ."

Stan was ready to give up. He put down the phone. Stan grabbed his keys. If he left right away he could get to the bank before it closed. He was walking out the door when his phone rang. He heard the answering machine click on, "This is Stan. Please leave a message after the beep." Then he heard Nancy's voice say, "Stan, I've been trying to call you all afternoon!"

The Dream Jar

"If you could have anything you wanted, what would you wish for?" Al asked Yolette.

"*Anything?*" Yolette asked.

"Anything," Al answered.

"I'd wish for more hours in each day," Yolette said.

"I think we'd all like that," laughed Al. "What would you wish for?" Yolette asked.

"I'd like to win the lottery," Al said.

"Millions of other people wish that, too," Yolette replied.

"Well, I can dream, can't I?" asked Al.

"I think there's a difference between wishes and dreams," Yolette said. "I think of wishes as things I want to magically happen. Like I wish I could eat ice cream every day. Or I wish I were a famous actress."

"Hey, that could happen," Al said. "You were great in that Community Playhouse show."

"I will never be famous," Yolette said, "because I'm not trying to become famous. I think I wish for things that I know are beyond my reach. Dreams are something else."

"What do you mean?" asked Al.

Yolette thought for a moment. "Dreams are things I can plan and work for. I dream of owning a house. I dream of having a beautiful flower garden. Those are things I know I can have if I work hard."

"I have a dream for you, too," said Al. "I dream of you getting on a plane to go visit your folks in Haiti."

"As long as we're dreaming about family," said Yolette, "how about a baby?"

Al's eyes opened wide. "A baby? Do you know how much babies cost?"

"If we waited until we could afford it, we'd never have a family," said Yolette.

"I guess you're right," said Al. "But first things first. We have to save enough money to buy the house. And then we'll plant that garden you dream of, and. . . ."

"Yes, Al," Yolette said, "our dream house comes first."

"Speaking of dreams, I dream of someday being debt free. I dream of having a job that I really like—a job where I could be promoted. I would make more money. Then I would be ready to talk about having a family." Al leaned back in his chair and closed his eyes. "I can just see myself driving up to our beautiful home. I can see the flower garden. I can see our kids running out to greet me."

"Kids?" Yolette asked. "How many kids?"

"Oh, three or four," Al replied. "And I'd want them all to go to college. That is a dream we can work for."

"I wish dreams didn't take so long to become real," said Yolette.

"If we work hard and budget our money, it won't take long. You'll see," said Al.

Then Yolette asked, "We're already saving for a house. How can we work toward so many dreams at once?"

"I'll tell you what I'll do," said Al. He went into the kitchen and brought out a jar. "I will put my pocket change in this jar. Anytime we have a little extra—even pennies—we'll put it in here." Al smiled. "It will add up. And we'll be saving toward our dreams. We'll call it our dream jar."

World of Machines

Yolette went to get a soda during a break from her class. She ran into Roberto and Stan near the vending machines. "Have you used this new snack machine yet?" Yolette asked them.

"No. But every time I turn around, there is a new machine I have to learn to use," said Roberto. "It's enough to drive me crazy."

"I know what you mean," said Yolette. "We live in a world of machines. They're supposed to *save* time but we *waste* a lot of time learning to use them!"

"And we waste even more time fixing them when they break," said Roberto.

"And keeping them working!" said Stan. "Do you know how long it took me to overhaul my lawn mower? It took me all day. I could have trimmed my lawn with scissors in the same amount of time!"

"Exactly! And think of the stress they cause us," said Yolette. "When I was in the computer lab the other day, I saw a young man screaming at his computer." She shook her head. "And he wasn't the only one." She looked around. "I confess," Yolette whispered, "I've yelled at my computer a few times. I even cried one day when my car wouldn't start."

"On TV commercials, machines always look so easy to use," said Stan. "Then you get one home and you realize that you have to read a whole book of instructions!"

"And you need a college degree to read them," said Yolette.

"How many machines do you think we deal with each day?" asked Roberto.

"Well, let's see," said Yolette. "I have a car, a washing machine, a dryer, a refrigerator, a toaster, a coffee maker, a microwave oven, a hair dryer, and. . . ."

Stan said, "At work, I have hedge trimmers, chain saws, weed trimmers, lawn mowers, tillers, and leaf blowers."

"Even my kids have machines," said Roberto. "At our house we have an electric train, a doll that walks and talks, TV video games, and dozens of toys that require batteries."

"You haven't mentioned the VCR your son Eddy had to show you how to operate," laughed Yolette.

"My latest battle with a machine is the telephone answering system," Roberto said. "I can't figure out how to set the time."

"Have you asked Eddy?" said Stan.

Everyone laughed.

"Seriously, I wonder if people were happier before we had all these fancy machines," Yolette said. "Or do you think they complained about other things? Weren't kids just as happy before video games were invented? And did people get bored sitting around talking or playing games before there was TV?"

"I don't know," said Stan, "Sometimes I wonder who's in charge now. Are machines working for us? Or are we here to work on the machines? And do they really save time? Or do we waste time figuring out how to work them?"

Roberto looked at his digital watch. "Hmm, my watch says 11:45. Is that the right time?"

"No," said Stan. "It's quarter past 12."

"Oh no!" said Roberto as he quickly grabbed his books. "My watch battery is dead. I'm going to be late for work!"

Yolette shook her head. "Machines!" she said. "We can't live with them, and we can't live without them."

Going Home

Roberto smiled as he drove northeast on Interstate 85. He and his family had a wonderful time in Georgia. The weather was perfect. Now they were on their way home. Roberto talked to Adela while Marco told stories to Eddy and Cruz in the back seat.

"I was so excited about this vacation," Adela said. "And now I am just as excited to be going home."

"Vacations are wonderful," said Roberto. "But after a while, I miss being home."

Adela was quiet for a few minutes. Then she said, "There are two places we call home now: Washington, D.C., and Puerto Rico. Which one feels more like home to you?"

Roberto replied, "Have you heard the saying, 'Home is where the heart is?' I feel that my heart is in the U.S. capital, Washington, D.C."

"But we have so many memories of Puerto Rico," said Adela. "And we still have family there."

"That's true," said Roberto. "But many people move away from the place they were born and raised. They leave home to start a life of their own in someplace new."

"When we first moved to Virginia, I was very homesick," said Adela. "I missed Puerto Rico. I missed my family and friends."

"But we have made new friends," said Roberto. "And in the last few years, some of our family members and old friends have moved here, too. Now we have relatives in Georgia."

"And our children are growing up," said Adela. "They will soon leave home to go to college. It makes me sad."

"I'm not going anywhere," Cruz interrupted. "I'm going to live at home forever."

"Me too," said Eddy. "I like Mama's cooking."

Roberto smiled over at Adela. "Well, how does that sound?" he asked her. "Our children will be living with us for another 50 or 60 years."

Roberto laughed. But Adela didn't laugh. "It's not that I don't want *anything* to change. I just wish *some* things could stay the same." She turned to look at the children in the back seat. "You two are going to college. You will grow up and get good jobs so you can take care of your father and me when we get old." Everyone laughed.

Then Marco spoke. "I like change," he said. "I think it's exciting that we have so many opportunities. In the future, I could move to another country. Home could be anyplace in the world. The Earth is my home." He thought for a minute. "But right now, I'm glad to live in the United States."

Before and After

Diep saw Stan at the grocery store. They were both pushing shopping carts piled with food. Diep said, "Would you like to come over and have dinner tonight with me and my kids?"

"That sounds like a good idea," Stan said. He reached into his shopping cart and held up a carton of ice cream. "I'll bring dessert."

After dinner, Stan was helping Diep's little girl, Lin, with her homework. "I don't understand the English language," Lin said. "You can say things so many different ways." She pointed to her lesson. "You can move words around to say the same thing. 'Before I go to bed, I turn out the light.' Or, 'I turn out the light before I go to bed.' Both sentences have the same meaning."

"I understand how that works," Stan said.

"Can you explain it to me?" Lin asked.

"First things first," said Stan. "Sentences are made of clauses. Some clauses can stand alone. They're *independent*. 'I bounced the ball.' There, one clause makes one sentence. But if I say, 'After I picked it up,' that's not a complete sentence. It's a *dependent* clause. It cannot stand alone."

"How can I tell whether a clause is dependent or independent?" Lin asked.

"Here's an example," Stan said. "What if I said to you, 'Before the game started.'"

"Before the game started, *what?*" asked Lin.

"See?" Stan replied. "'Before the game started' can't stand alone. It is a *dependent* clause. It needs the help of an *independent* clause in order to make a complete sentence.

"Your lesson is about dependent time clauses," Stan continued. "A time clause starts with a word like *before, after,* or *when.* These clauses tell *when* something happens."

The little girl began to fidget.

"Look," said Stan. "Let's take your sentence that begins with 'before.' *Before I go to bed* is a time clause. You can put the time clause at the beginning of your sentence or at the end."

Diep walked into the room. She said to her daughter, "Now it is time for you to go to bed. And before you go to bed, you must brush your teeth. Did you hear me? You must brush your teeth before you go to bed!"

Everyone laughed. Then Lin said, "And after I go to bed, I want a story. I want a story after I go to bed." Then she ran into the kitchen. "But before I go to bed, I want a snack. I want a snack before I go to bed!"

Then Lin smiled and said, "Now I think I understand. I think I understand now!"

Coping with Emotions

Stan and Diep sat on the grass between classes. They saw Roberto walking across campus.

"Hey, Roberto," yelled Stan. "Come sit with us. You look like you need a break."

Roberto sat down. He looked sad.

"What's the matter?" asked Diep.

"Work relationships are difficult," said Roberto, sighing.

"I know what you mean," said Diep. "When you think you are doing the right thing, it turns out to be wrong."

"People are hard to understand. It can be very frustrating," said Stan. He thought for a minute. "But sometimes it is just embarrassing."

"I know all about being embarrassed," said Roberto. "I spilled soup all over a customer the other day."

"Oh, no! What did you do?" Stan asked.

"Well, I wanted to crawl under the table and hide," said Roberto.

"What did your boss say?" asked Diep.

"He was angry at first," said Roberto. "But at least he didn't fire me."

"My boss is a nice guy," said Stan. "But the men I work with are careless and lazy. I get so mad at them sometimes!"

"Getting along with co-workers can be difficult. I wonder what the best way is to handle relationship problems," said Diep.

Yolette walked up just then. "Whose relationship problems?" she asked. She sat down on the grass with the others.

"Mine," Stan, Roberto, and Diep all said.

Diep filled Yolette in on what they had been talking about.

"Well, I'm no expert," said Yolette, "but I do know that sometimes people's feelings aren't obvious. Just the other night, Al broke a dinner plate. I got angry, and I said some things I never should have said. Later, after I thought about it, I realized I wasn't mad about the broken plate. Then Al and I had a long talk. And I admitted that I was really stressed out about some new tasks I'm struggling with at work. I guess I was trying to hide my feelings."

"People react differently when they are under pressure," said Stan. "I tend to lose my temper. But I have another friend who gets very quiet when he's upset."

"I just want to run away," said Diep.

"And I feel embarrassed," said Roberto.

There was a long silence.

Stan looked at Yolette. "So, if you could do it all over again, how would you handle that situation with Al?" he asked her.

"First of all, I should have known how tense I was," Yolette answered. "I'd been gritting my teeth all day. I should have waited until I calmed down, and then had a talk with Al. He always knows just what to say to make me feel better. I'm sure I could have just talked away my tension!"

Yolette laughed and then she continued. "I think the best thing, for any relationship, is honesty. And the worst thing in a relationship—whether it's parents and kids, husband and wife, boss and employee, friends, or co-workers—is when people hide their real feelings. We all make mistakes. And we all have bad days. We have to learn to admit when we're wrong and be honest about our feelings." Everyone nodded in agreement.

Pros and Cons

Roberto was telling Adela about his conversation with Stan and Diep about MediKit. "I couldn't think of a good reason for that company to come to Herndon. But I listened to Stan and Diep, and I began to see that there was another side to the issue."

"There are pros and cons to everything," Adela said to Roberto. "I don't know if anything is ever the 100-percent-right thing to do."

"What do you mean?" Roberto asked.

"For example, we'd like to buy a house," Adela said. "But we can't just say let's buy a house. We have to look at all the arguments *for* and *against* it. If there were more reasons we shouldn't buy a house now than reasons we should, then we would wait."

"What does this have to do with MediKit coming to town?" asked Roberto.

"All those pros and cons," said Adela. "Having that company here is both good and bad. I like to take the children to those woods to play. But I'm afraid of chemicals polluting our water and air. On the other hand, they say the new plant will employ 500 people. It's possible that I could get a good job there and be able to save more money toward a house." She frowned at Roberto. "Why is it so hard to make a decision?"

"I think it's because any one decision can affect many other things," Roberto said. "Everything seems to be connected to something else. We are faced with difficult decisions every day. And just to make one decision, we have to weigh the pros and cons and consider what effect our decision will have on other aspects of our lives. There is no way out of that."

Roberto smiled at Adela and said, "But one thing is always right. It's always right to care about other people. I don't think twice about doing something nice for one of my friends."

Adela smiled. "You're right," she said. "Some of the easiest decisions I make are about other people. It's the personal decisions I have the most trouble with."

"Would it be difficult for you to decide whether to go out to dinner with me tonight?" Roberto asked.

Adela gave Roberto a serious look. "Well, I would have to consider all the pros and cons," said Adela. "Let's see, on the positive side, I wouldn't have to worry about what to cook tonight. But on the negative side, I might have trouble deciding what to wear. And where will we go? Should we bring Eddy and Cruz? What time should we leave? See! Just thinking about it forces me to consider making other decisions!"

"Let me make this easy for you, Adela," Roberto laughed. "I won't take no for an answer. We're leaving right now. The kids are coming with us. You're wearing what you have on. And we're going to Tony's Pizza. And I can even order for you so you won't have to make any decisions tonight!"

Play It Again

Yolette came to visit Adela. Adela was folding clothes. "Eddy and Cruz are outgrowing all their clothes," Adela said. "When I think of what I paid for those clothes, even at the thrift shop, it makes me want to cry."

"I know what you mean," said Yolette. "I'm outgrowing all my clothes, too. Too much ice cream."

Adela laughed. "I don't believe that," she said. Then she added, "But at least you can lose weight and fit back into your clothes. I have to go out and buy new clothes for the kids. I try to recycle the old ones, though. I give them to the Salvation Army. That way some other kids can wear them until they outgrow them."

"Wouldn't it be great if we never wasted anything?" Yolette asked. "I mean, why don't we recycle everything over and over until it's all used up? We waste so much. I hate throwing anything away."

"Did you hear what Diep did? She suggested that the hospital donate outdated forms and stationery to local schools," said Adela. "Cruz told me that her teacher is using blank hospital file cards to make flashcards. It was such a great idea that Diep got a reward."

"Recycling just makes sense," said Yolette. "Recycled products can be used to make new things. Did you know that recycled plastic bottles are being used to make everything from clothing to carpeting?"

"Really?" asked Adela. "I read that old tires can be made into welcome mats."

"Yes. And recycled rags can be turned into paper," said Yolette.

Adela put the stacks of children's clothes into a box. "Well, I hope some other kids have as much fun wearing these clothes as Cruz and Eddy did." She smiled and put the last stack of clothes in a box. As Yolette helped her carry out the boxes, Adela said, "I have some leftovers from last night. How about if I recycle them into some lunch for us?"

Man's Work

Marco was very upset after the accident. He was helping his Aunt Adela carry groceries into the house one day. He started complaining about how much the car repairs would cost.

"Marco," Adela said, "you're lucky. It's only a car. Nobody got hurt. That's the important thing."

"Yes, I know," Marco admitted. "But I still have to pay for the repairs."

"Yes, you do have to pay the garage," said Adela. "But you've learned some things that should save you money in the long run. You know that you should bring your car to the garage as soon as the brakes start to squeak. And you've learned how to change the oil and transmission fluid yourself."

"The mechanic told me that it's also a good idea to drain and refill the radiator before winter," said Marco.

"I bet I could help you," said Adela. "There are instructions in the repair manual."

"No, I'll do it. Working with cars is a man's job," said Marco. "Besides, you don't want to get all dirty."

Adela just raised her eyebrows and went into the kitchen. She was putting the groceries away when Marco yelled from the garage, "How do I get this cap off?"

Adela shook her head and reached in the toolbox. She got out a wrench and handed it to Marco.

Adela didn't hear from Marco for about an hour. When he came back in, he was soaking wet. He smelled like antifreeze.

Adela shouted, "Don't come in here like that. You'll get antifreeze all over everything. What happened?"

Marco stood in the garage door. "Well, first I had a hard time getting the cap off. Then when it came off, antifreeze poured all over me. I forgot to have a drain pan ready."

"It looks like you've learned another lesson, Marco," Adela said. "Next time maybe you won't be so quick to refuse my help. And you're right—I wouldn't want to get *that* dirty!"

For the Love of Wheels

Yolette stood in line waiting for the bus. She was very tired after a long day at work. She watched the cars driving by. I wish I had a car, she thought. She began to daydream about owning her own sports car.

Later that evening she and Al sat on the couch, watching TV. They saw a commercial for a bright red sports car. "I would love to have a car like that," she told Al excitedly.

"A sports car?" asked Al. "Where would you put our children, and the groceries, and the plants for our flower garden?" He smiled and put his arm around Yolette.

The phone rang. Yolette picked it up. "Hello," she said.

"Thank heaven, there is a real person on the line!" Stan said.

"What do you mean?" Yolette asked.

"I've been making calls all day long and once again all I get are computerized phone messages," Stan said. "I need some advice."

"Well, come on over," said Yolette. "Al and I would be glad to talk to you."

When Stan came, he told them he was trading in his sports car for a van. He told them about his research. He explained about comparing finance plans. "What do you think I should do?" he asked.

Yolette said, "I had no idea there was so much to think about when you buy a car." Then she smiled and asked, "What are you going to do with your sports car?"

"I'll either sell it or trade it in," said Stan.

"How much would you ask for it?" asked Al. Yolette squealed with excitement.

Al smiled. "Well, we don't have any children yet. Or the house and garden."

"It's a few years old," Stan replied. "But I've seen ads for similar cars. They sell for around $4,000."

When Yolette thought about the money, her excitement faded. "It would be nice to have a car," she said. "But I think the house comes first. Al, let's concentrate on saving toward our dream house and let someone else enjoy the sports car."

Crime and Fear

The week that Quang was mugged, 11 other muggings were also reported. In the days following the muggings, crime and fear became popular topics of conversation. People talked about nothing else. Everyone had a different solution to the problems. Some made plans to protect themselves. Some talked about what the community could do to make things safer. But the mugger had still not been caught.

Diep had to sit and hold her children tight every night before they went to sleep. One evening, Diep's daughter asked, "Do muggers ever ride the school bus?"

"No. You don't have to worry about that," said Diep reassuringly.

"But Uncle Quang wasn't worried either," said Lin. "And that man hurt him."

"I'll protect you," said her brother Hai. "I'm big. If I see a mugger, I'll kick him." The boy kicked at the air. But Diep noticed that Hai didn't play outside anymore.

After the children were asleep, Diep called Adela. "I need your help," said Diep. "It's about Lin and Hai. They are very frightened now after Quang's mugging. I don't know what to say to them."

"Why don't you all come over for dinner tomorrow?" said Adela. "Eddy and Cruz are worried, too. Maybe we can talk with them together."

When the Trans arrived, they smelled something wonderful. Adela said, "I've baked a cake. It's called a friendship cake."

"What's a friendship cake?" asked Lin.

"It's a cake that is shared by friends," said Adela. "Now, let's sit down and talk. I have a question for all of you. What is a friend?"

"Somebody you like," said Lin.

"Somebody who likes you," said Hai.

"A guy you like to play ball with," said Eddy.

Cruz said quietly, "A friend is someone you like to talk to. Someone who never tells your secrets."

"You are all right. Friends take care of each other," said Adela.

After dinner, everyone had cake and juice. Adela and Diep drank coffee. Then Adela said, "We have a problem. There is someone in our town who is not a friend to us."

"I know," said Hai. "He's the man who hurt Uncle Quang and took his money."

"Is he your friend?" asked Adela.

"No," all the children said together.

"Would you like him for a friend?" asked Adela.

"No way!" shouted the children.

"Maybe he doesn't have any friends," added Diep. "Maybe he does bad things because he is alone and unhappy."

"That makes me feel sorry for him," said Cruz. "I wonder what it feels like not to have friends."

"It must be terrible. But most people *do* have friends," said Adela. "And friends take care of each other. They watch out for each other. And most people are helpful and loving. We can depend on them."

"But what about the bad man?" Hai asked. "Even if he doesn't have friends, he's scary. I'm afraid he'll come back."

"There are some bad people in the world," said Adela. "But there are more good people. We have to be careful. But we don't have to be afraid." She smiled. "We can be brave *and* careful. And we will watch out for each other. We have to be good friends and protect each other."

The children went into the bedroom to play and Adela turned to Diep. "We should be careful that we don't let our own fear frighten the children," she said. "They understand more than we think they do."

"But, Adela, I *am* frightened. I'm afraid to go out alone." Diep looked down. "I came to the U.S. to be safe. I do not feel safe anymore."

"Diep, remember all the wonderful people you've met here," Adela said. "You are surrounded by good friends. This mugger is only one man. And he just wanted some money. He is not after you or your children."

"How can I assure my children that they are safe?" asked Diep.

"In time, they will be less afraid," said Adela. "And if the police catch the mugger, that will help. In the meantime, we will just love and protect our children. We can teach them safety rules. We can tell them not to talk to strangers and not to walk alone anywhere."

"Maybe if my children see that I am brave, they too will be brave," said Diep.

"Yes, that's right," Adela said. "And soon they will realize that they have family and many friends who love them. They will learn to trust their friends and be happy. They will learn it from you."

House and Home

Yolette couldn't even eat breakfast. She paced back and forth in the bedroom. At last, it was the day she and Al were going to the bank to get financing for their new house. "How can you be so calm?" she asked Al.

"Yolette, it's just a house," Al said, pretending to yawn.

Yolette threw a pillow at him. "You are faking. You're just as excited as I am."

"It is a big day for us, that's for sure," Al said. "Should we dress up? Or should we wear old clothes so they will think we really need this money?"

"I think we should just be ourselves," Yolette said. "I'm a little scared. What if they don't give us the loan?"

"They will," said Al. "According to the bank chart, we qualify. And we have a good credit rating."

Al and Yolette took the bus to the bank. It was just as Al said. They came out of the bank with the paperwork to buy their new house.

"Can we go get ice cream?" asked Yolette.

"Sure," Al said. "Let's celebrate. Then we can walk over and look at the house again."

Yolette and Al stood on the sidewalk eating ice cream. They talked about how their lives would change when the house became theirs. "Can't you see us here in a few years with our kids running around? Do you think we'll miss our little apartment?" Yolette asked.

"I think we might miss how quiet the apartment was," Al laughed.

"Al, our place won't be quiet for very long," Yolette said. "I think I'm pregnant."

Al threw his arms around Yolette and hugged her tight. "So that's why you eat so much ice cream! Wow. We're going to have a new house and a new baby," he said. "I'm so happy."

A few weeks later, the moving truck pulled up in front of the Jamisons' new house. Yolette started unpacking the boxes as fast as she could. "What's your hurry?" Al asked. "We have the rest of our lives to get settled."

"I want it done now, Al," said Yolette. "I want to sit down in our house tonight and feel at home."

Al helped Yolette unpack, and they ordered a pizza for supper. Al set the table with paper plates. Yolette felt such happiness she almost cried. "This is the best meal I've ever had," she said.

Just as they finished eating, chimes rang.

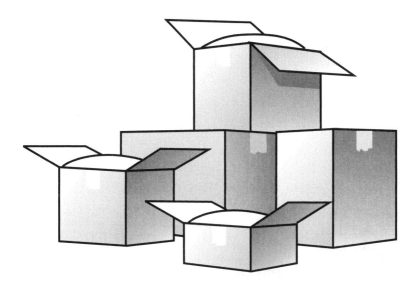

"What's that?" asked Al.

"I think it's the doorbell," Yolette said. "It's the first visitor to our new house. Let's go see who it is." They both went to the front door and opened it.

A man stood on the porch holding a big box. "Is this the Jamison residence?" he asked.

"Yes," Al said. "This is the Jamison house."

"I have a package for Mrs. Jamison," he said. "Sign here, please."

Yolette signed. She looked at Al and smiled. "I wonder what it is," she said. Al set the box down and opened it. Yolette pulled out a rosebush. An attached card read, "May all your dreams come true. Love, Al."

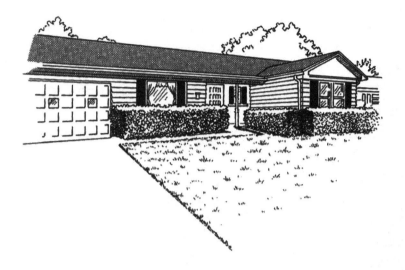

Housewarming

Yolette took a good look at herself in the mirror. "Already my clothes are getting tight," she said to Al. She patted her belly and frowned.

"I think you look beautiful," Al said. "Just think, in only a few more months we will be parents."

"First a house and now a baby," Yolette said. "Dreams do come true."

"You taught me something about that," Al said. "Dreams can come true if you want them badly enough to work for them. Wishes are different. It would be nice if we got our wishes, but we can't do much about them."

"Are you scared, now that our life is changing so much?" Yolette asked.

"A little," said Al. "I mean, what if this baby is a girl? I could handle a boy, but what would I do with a little girl? That's scary."

"Why is a baby girl so scary?" Yolette asked.

Al folded his arms and looked stern. "I can't imagine how hard it would be to protect her, care for her, and then watch her grow up, get married, and leave," he said.

"She's not even born yet, and you're worried about her wedding?" Yolette laughed. "Boys get married, too."

"Boys are different. You don't worry about them so much." Al thought for a minute. "Well, maybe I'd be worried if he wanted to ride a motorcycle or bungee jump or. . . ." He stopped and looked around the room. "Yolette, what would we do if our child got sick, or if I lost my job and we couldn't pay the bills?"

Yolette put her arms around Al. "We'll do fine," she said. "My grandmother used to tell me that life is full of 'ifs'. It's what you do after the 'if' that counts. If someone gives you lemons, make lemonade. If you fall down, pick yourself up. If you lose your job, you'll get another one." She patted Al's back.

"I suppose you're right," said Al.

"Besides," Yolette added, "'ifs' can be good, too. What if our daughter becomes a doctor or an astronaut? What if our son grows up to be a famous artist or what if he wins a Nobel Prize?"

Then Yolette looked thoughtful. "Hmm . . . you know what I want right now?" she asked.

Al shook his head. He looked worried.

"Ice cream," said Yolette, grinning.

"You always want the same thing," Al said. They both laughed. "Maybe someday you can own your own ice cream parlor and have ice cream every day!"

"That's what I've always wished for!" said Yolette. She leaned over to give Al a kiss.

Just then the doorbell rang. Yolette opened the door.

"Surprise!" shouted the group on the porch. There stood Diep, her two kids, Quang, Stan, Roberto, Adela, Cruz, and Eddy.

"Happy new house!" shouted Stan. He held out a big basket of fruit.

"I made a picture for your wall," said Eddy.

"And I baked a cake," said Adela. "A housewarming cake. This is a true celebration. We're celebrating your new house and our friendship."

Everyone came into the house, laughing and talking all at once.

"We bought you a housewarming gift," said Stan. He set a large box on the table. "You open it, Yolette."

Yolette pulled off the paper and then clapped her hands. "An ice cream maker!" she shouted. Then she turned to Al. "Al, they bought us an ice cream maker!"

Al smiled and put his arm around Yolette. "Sometimes even wishes come true."

"Now can we have cake?" Eddy asked.

[7]